THE BROONS

© D.C. Thomson & Co., Ltd, 2016
Published by D.C. Thomson Annuals Ltd in 2016
D.C. Thomson Annuals Ltd, 185 Fleet Street London EC4A 2HS

IF WI' DAPHNE YOU HAVE A TIFF, THINGS CAN END UP WI' A BIFF!

THE BAIRN CANNA GET IN THE BAND, UNTIL MAW LENDS A HELPIN' HAND.

THE POOR LASS IS FEELING FRUMPY,
GOING GREY AND LOOKING LUMPY.

ARE THE OLDEST AND THE YOUNGEST BROON THE HAPPIEST FOLK IN AUCHENTOGLE TOON?

PAW BROON'S WINNIN' STREAK, MAY TURN OUT A BITTY BLEAK.

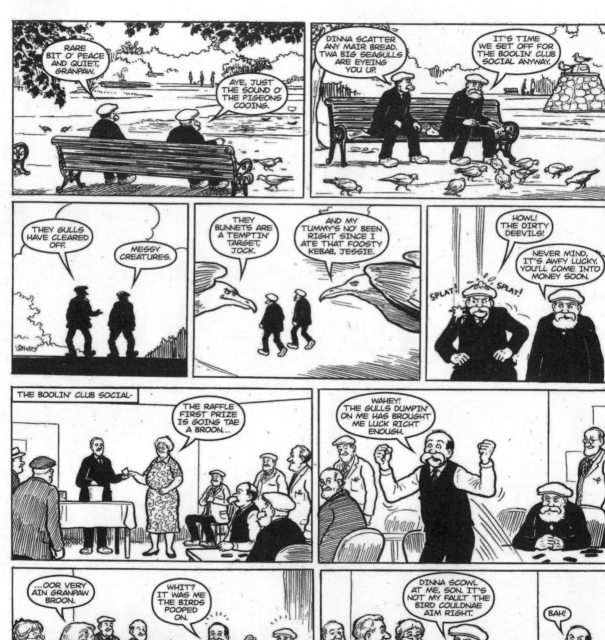

WHAT'S THIS AWFY SIGHT, MAKING THE YOUNG ANES SCREAM IN FRIGHT?

BEST PROCEED WI' CAUTION,
IF YE TAMPER WI' THE WASHIN'.

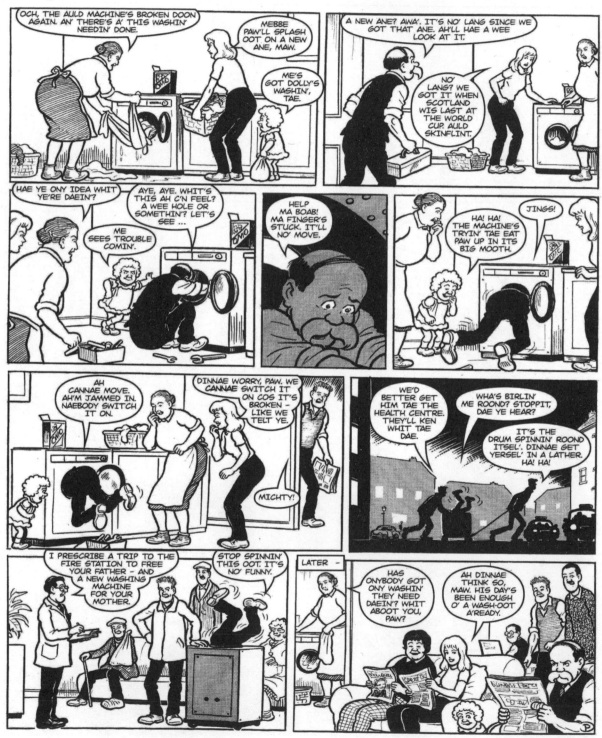

PAW SEEMS TO HAE A MAGICAL TOUCH,
WHICH POOR MAW DISNAE APPRECIATE MUCH.

THE BROONS PEACEFUL, HIGHLAND RETREAT ROCKS TAE THE SOUND OF THE BLEAT.

GRANPAW MUST FIND OUT HIS FATE,
HIS LIBRARY BOOK IS TEN YEARS LATE.

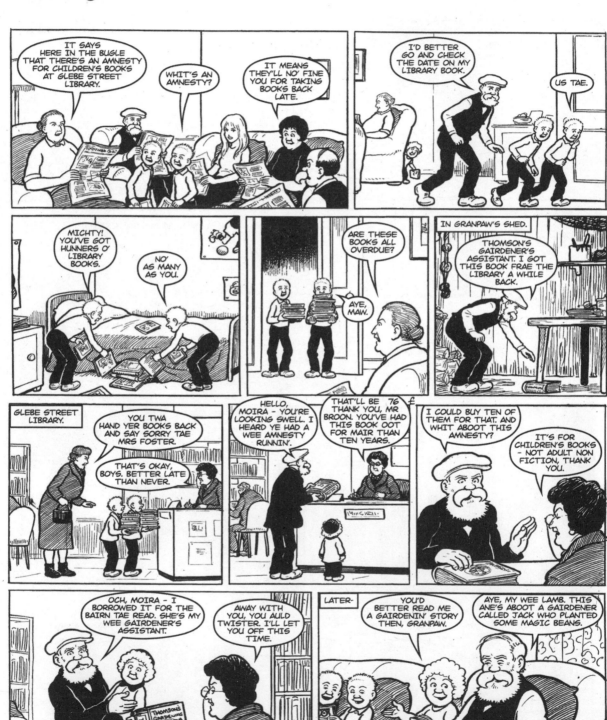

IT TICKLES GRANPAW'S RIBS,
TELLING HIS AULD CRONIES FIBS.

GRANPAW'S PLAN IS THE VERY DAB,
FOR HELPING DAPHNE FIGHT THE FLAB.

PAW BROON IS AFTER THE TRUTH,
ON WHY THE COTTAGE HAS A DROUTH.

A CUFFLINK'S LOST, HEAR PAW CRY,
TURNING THE HOOSE INTAE A PIG STY.

THE YOUNG BROONS ARE AT A LOSS
TO MASTER THE ART OF THE PANCAKE TOSS.

THE BAIRN'S TALE OF DAPHNE'S CRUSH, MAKES HER BIGGEST SISTER BLUSH.

OH, DAPHNE, I THINK YE'RE AWFY BRAW.

AND I THINK YOU'RE A WUDDLY, DUDDLY...

...CUDDLY BOY.

SSSH!

DAE YOU KEN WHIT TIME IT IS, YOUNG MAN?

PA-AW!

I'M JUST LEAVING, MR BROON. WHAT WITH IT BEING A WORKING DAY TOMORROW.

NICE TAE MEET YE, ER... WHA EVER YE ARE.

WHIT'S WRANG WI' HIM? I ONLY ASKED HIM THE TIME?

DID YE HUMPH! I'M NO' TWELVE, YE KEN.

WHY ARE YOU NO' IN BED? HAE YOU BEEN THERE SPYIN' ON ME ALL THE TIME?

NAW, I CAME BACK FOR MY DOLLY THEN YOU CAME IN.

AYE, RIGHT.

DINNA GET ON TO THE BAIRN. WHAT WERE THE TWA O' YE YAPPIN' ABOOT ALL THIS TIME ONYWAY?

IF YOU MUST KNOW WE WERE TALKING ABOOT FAMILY – OOR KITH AND KIN.

IT'S TRUE, MAW. HE ASKED FOR A KITH AND DAPHNE SAID YE KIN.

HA! HA!

YE WEE BESOM!

FRAE THE MOUTH O' BAIRNS.

THE RARE SIGHT O' SCOTTISH SUN, SHOULD BE A REASON FOR GOOD FUN.

IT'S VERY EASY TO TELL,
MAW BROON KNOWS HER FAMILY WELL.

PAW THINKS THE LADS ARE TAKING THE MICK, SAYING HE NEEDS A WALKING STICK.

THE BROONS ARE TRAINING FOR THE KILTWALK. TRAINING CAMP IS THE BUT AN' BEN.

SOME TRAINING CAMP - THE WIND UP HERE NEAR BLAWS YE BACKWARDS.

BUT WHEN IT DROPS THIS BONNIE PLACE IS MADE FOR WALKERS.

ARE YOU READY FOR A HIKE THEN, PAW?

TAK' THEY WALKING POLES, PAW. THEY'LL HELP KEEP YOU GOING.

WHAT ARE YE TRYING TAE SAY, JOE - THAT I'M SAE AULD I'M NEEDING A STICK?

NAW, PAW. YOUNG FOWK USE THEM TAE - THEY HELP YOU KEEP PACE.

OH, WELL THEN...

THESE POLES DO HELP YE ALANG.

WELL, YOU'RE NO' GETTING ONY YOUNGER WHETHER YOU LIKE IT OR NOT.

PAW'S NO' STOPPING FOR A BITE TAE EAT.

AYE, THE WALKING POLES HAVE REALLY HELPED THE AULD MAN.

I HEARD THAT.

MY WALKING POLES HAE FOUND A BOGGY BIT, LASS. WE'LL SIT HERE AND HAE OOR CUPPIE.

JUST IN CASE YOUR BROTHERS AND SISTERS ARE NO' AS OBSERVANT AS YOU AND ME.

HA! HA! THEY'RE A' STUCK, PAW.

THE WALKING POLES HAVE COME IN HANDY FOR YOU ANES TAE.

HELP MAH BOAB! WE'RE SINKING.

BUT I'M SINKING FASTER THAN YOU!

HEN AND JOE ARE NEAR DRIVEN DAFT,
WATCHIN' A DRAMA THEY THINK IS SAFT.

GRANPAW BROON DISNAE CARE MUCH,
ABOOT TRYING TO STAY IN TOUCH.

PAW DECIDES THAT HE'S THE ONE,
TAE SING THE SONGS THAT WERE SUCH FUN.

A MONEY MAKING SCHEME THAT CANNA FAIL,
IS SELLING STUFF AT THE CAR BOOT SALE.

THE AULD ANES ARE OOT TAE PLAY,
ON THIS BRAW IRISH DAY.

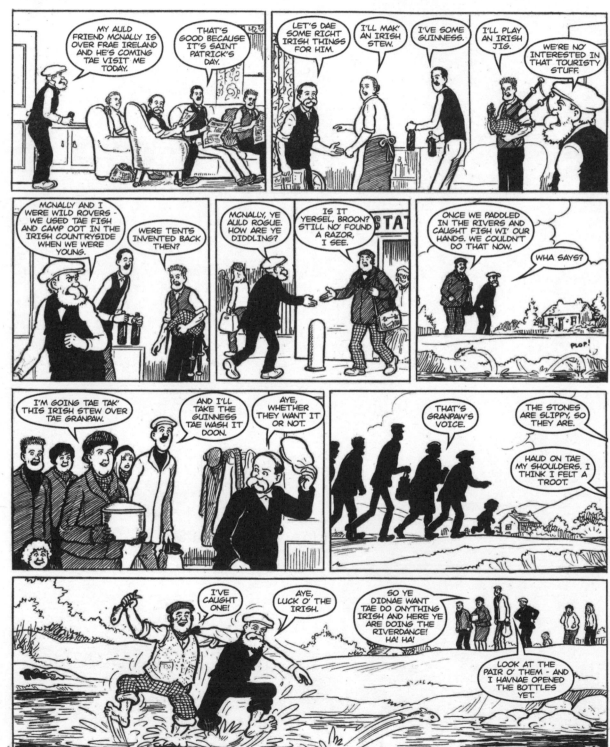

DAPH DOESN'T CARE ABOUT HER FIGURE,
SHE SEEMS INTENT ON GETTING BIGGER.

WALKING THE HILLS IS NOT CHILD'S PLAY,
YOU CAN EASILY LOSE YOUR WAY.

MY BRAW LADDIES ARE GOING ON THE KILTWALK. I'M PROUD O' YOU ALL.

I'M DOING THE KILTWALK AS WELL, MAW. ARE YOU COMING, DAPHNE?

WHIT?

ER, NO... THE SUNDAY POST WON NEWSPAPER O' THE YEAR. I WAS AT THEIR PARTY AND LOST MY KILT. I'LL DO THE FIRST AID.

AT THE WALK...

JUST HAE A WEE WARM-UP BEFORE THE WALK STARTS.

STRETCH

JINGS! WHA'S THAT SMASHER BESIDE HEN AND THE LADDIES?

KILTWA

HELLO, I'M THE FIRST AID HERE. DO YOU NEED ONYTHING? A WET SPONGE? A MASSAGE? A NICHT OOT AT THE DANCIN' AND A CUDDLE ON THE WAY HAME?

NAW, I'M FINE, THANKS.

AYE, YOU'RE NO' HALF.

MICHTY. WHAT TRIPPED ME UP THERE?

YOU'VE FALLEN OWER MY HEEL, YOU POOR LAD.

TRIP!

YOU'D BETTER LET ME LOOK AFTER YOU.

SPLAT!

DAPHNE BROON, YOU'RE SHAMELESS.

I'M FINE. REALLY, I AM.

NAW, YOU MIGHT HAE A CONCUSSION OR A BROKEN TRAINER OR SOMETHING.

I'M AWA'.

COME BACK. YOU HAVEN'T HAD THE KISS OF LIFE YET.

SHE'S TURNED THE KILTWALK INTO A KILTRUN.

SHE'S NO' EVEN IN THE WALK AND SHE'LL STILL BE THE FIRST BROON TO FINISH.

D.

IT'S THERE FOR ALL TO SEE,
GREENY POLES ARE NO' WHAT THEY USED TAE BE.

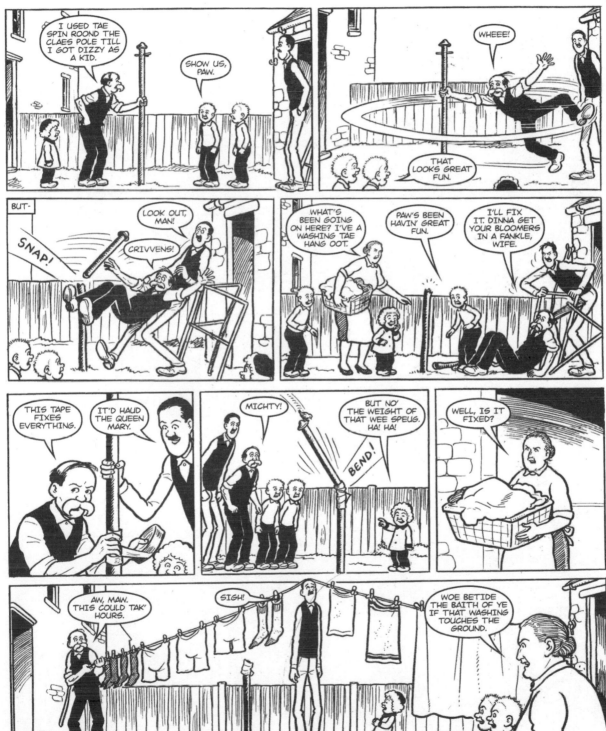

MAW BROON STILL KNOWS WHAT'S GOOD, EVEN FOR HER GROWN UP BROOD.

IS GRANPAW'S TONGUE TIED IN KNOTS –
OR IS IT HIS TEETH THAT CAN'T SPEAK SCOTS?

GRANPAW BROON MUST BE AWFY ILL, IF THAT'S HIM WORKING OOT HIS WILL.

SITTING ON ITS OWN WEE NEST
IS THE BUT AN' BEN'S VERY WELCOME GUEST.

A T-SHIRT MINNIE MOUSE HAS SIGNED,
IS NO' WHAT THE BAIRN HAS IN MIND.

IT'S EASY TO STEP ON TO A BOAT, THE TRICK IS TO KEEP THE THING AFLOAT.

PAW HADNAE PLANNED
TO STAND HIS HAND.

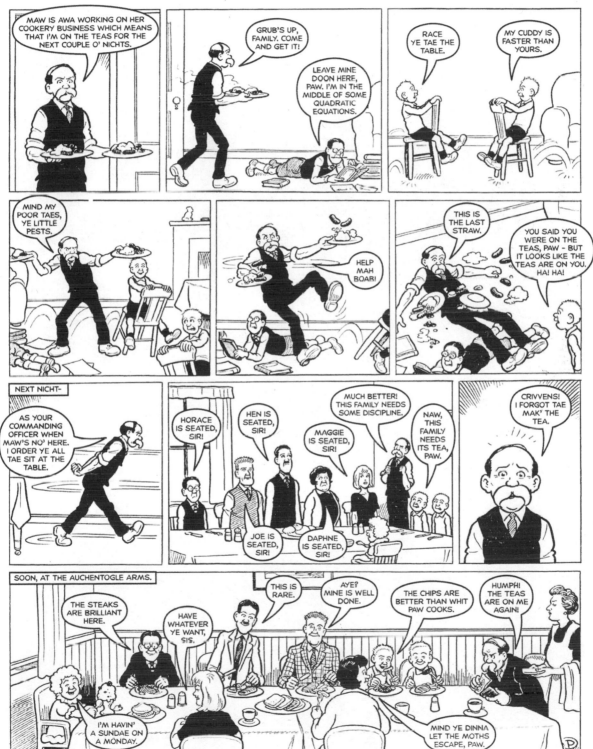

THE PLACE TAE LEARN A' THE NEWS
IS OWER ANE OF MAW BROON'S STEWS.

GRANPAW'S NOT THE MAN TO MEET, WHEN YOU'RE LOOKING FOR FREE HEAT.

WHIT A DRAUGHT COMES IN THAT WINDAE. YOUR PAPER IS GETTING BLOWN AWA.

IS IT? I NEVER NOTICED.

DRAUGHT!

THIS HOOSE IS FREEZING.

DRAUGHT!

GO AND PUT ANOTHER JUMPER ON IF YOU'RE CAULD, DAPHNE.

I'M MAGGIE! YOU THOUGHT I WAS DAPHNE BECAUSE I'VE GOT FOWER JUMPERS ON ALREADY.

YOU'RE TOO YOUNG TAE BE CAULD THEN.

HEN, TURN UP THE RADIATOR WHILE I PUT COAL ON THE FIRE. THIS IS LIKE SITTING IN THE ARCTIC.

HEAVENS, WUMMAN! DAE YE THINK I'M MADE OF MONEY?

IF YE STOPPED SITTING ABOOT AND TOOK SOME EXERCISE YE'D SOON GET WARM.

WE'RE FINE NOW.

I'M AWA FOR A BRISK WALK. THAT'LL KEEP ME WARM FOR FREE.

LOOK IN ON GRANPAW AND SEE HOW HE'S MANAGING THE CAULD.

GRANPAW'S MANAGING FINE BECAUSE HE'S IN THE WARM PUB.

HELLO, SON. I'LL GIE YOU A GAME BEFORE YOU SIT DOON.

WE'RE PLAYING DRAUGHTS TONIGHT.

CLACK!

CLACK!

CLACK!

CLACK!

YOU LOSE SO AWA AND GET THE DRAMS IN, AND MAYBE SOME PEANUTS TAE.

CRIVVENS! DRAUGHTS COST ME MONEY NAE MATTER WHAUR I GO.

MAW BROON WAS NEVER LIGHT AS AIR AND PAW'S NO' YOUNG ONY MAIR.

THERE'S MONEY TO BE MADE
IF GRANPAW CAN JOIN THE TOURIST TRADE.

THE STRANGER SKULKING AT THE BROONS' HAME, IS CAUGHT BY A VERY UNLIKELY DAME.

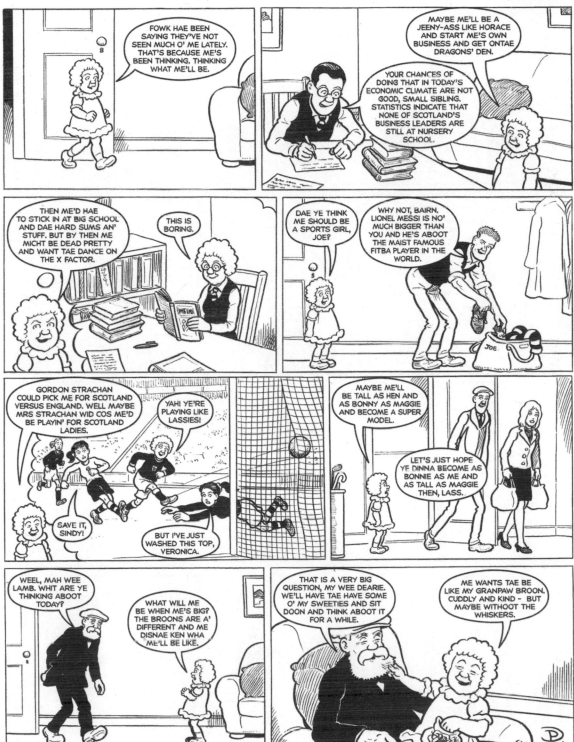

LISTEN TO GRANPAW ROAR,
WHEN SOMEONE OPENS THE LITTLE DOOR.

I'VE INVITED OOR PAL WILLOW UP TAE THE BUT AN' BEN THIS WEEKEND.

I'LL INSTRUCT YOU IN THE ART OF MEDITATION IF YOU DO ME BED AND BREAKFAST.

AYE, RIGHT.

DOWN IN THE GLEN–

THIS REMOTE PLACE IS PERFECT FOR MEDITATION, MY CHILDREN.

IT'S OOR WEE BIT OF HEAVEN.

EVERYONE MUST FIND THEIR OWN SPACE TO MEDITATE IN.

MICHTY! I HEAR A MUCKLE CLEG.

UUUUUUM!

SSSHHHT! IT'S US MEDITATING, YE SCUNNER.

UMMMMMMMMMM!

YE SOUND LIKE A SWARM O' BEASTIES.

AND YOU'RE NOT MEDITATING ON ALL MY CLEAN TOWELS.

OCH, MAW!

TRULY YOU ARE AN EARTH MOTHER, MAW BROON.

MAYBE, BUT YOU'RE STILL NOT GETTING EARTH ON MY CLEAN TOWELS. THERE'S MAYBE SOME AULD SACKS IN THE SHED.

LET US LOOK IN THESE SHEDS, CHILDREN OF THE GLEN.

ER, DINNA GO IN THERE, WILLOW.

AHA! OLD MAN OF THE BROONS - I SEE YOU HAVE FOUND YOUR SPACE FOR MEDITATION.

THUMP!

NAW, THIS IS MY SPACE FOR CONSTIPATION! DAFT LADDIE!

THERE'S A SECRET AT THE BUT AN' BEN,
KNOWN ONLY TAE THE BRAW BROONS MEN.

PAW BROON MAKES AN AWFY HASH, AT TRYING TAE SAVE HIMSELF SOME CASH.

WHIT'S THIS? NAE FIRE ON? YE KEN IT'S MY DAY AFF AND I LIKE A GUID FIRE.

THERE'S NAE KINDLING TAE LIGHT THE FIRE. YOU CAN BUY SOME AT THE SUPERMARKET IF YE'VE A MIND.

ME AND MAW ARE HAVIN' A GIRLIE DAY OOT.

I'M NOT PAYING FOR A FEW WEE STRIPS O' WOOD. THERE MUST BE SOMETHING LYING ABOOT.

SO—

AHA! THE BAIRN'S AULD COT – IT'LL BREAK INTO KINDLERS NAE PROBLEM.

IT'S JUST BEEN LYING ABOOT GATHERING DUST.

MICHTY! IT'LL NO' BURN YET IT'S BONE DRY.

YOU SILLY MAN – COTS ARE MADE O' SPECIALLY TREATED WOOD THAT WON'T BURN AT ALL.

SILLY, SILLY MAN.

AND I PROMISED THE BAIRN SHE COULD USE THAT AULD COT FOR THE NEW DOLLY WE BOUGHT.

AT THE TOY SHOP.

YOU CAN BUY THE BAIRN A DOLLY COT THEN TREAT US TAE TEA AT THE CAFE.

AND I'LL STILL HAVE TAE BUY KINDLERS.

PAW BROON, WHIT'LL WE DAE WI' YOU?

SCOTLAND'S HERO IS IN A STEW, UNTIL GRANPAW BROON'S SPEEDY RESCUE.

HEN, TRYING TO GET FRESH AIR, ENDS UP WITH HIS FEET SO SAIR.

GRANPAW'S HIRED US THIS PEOPLE CARRIER. ALL ABOARD FOR THE BUT AN' BEN.

I'M NO SQUEEZIN' IN THERE. I'LL HIKE. I'M WANTING FRESH AIR.

JINGS! I'M ONLY TWA MILES OOT O' AUCHENTOGLE AND MY FEET ARE A' BLISTERS.

NAE ROOM FOR YE NOW, HEN. WE'VE BEEN TAE THE SUPERMARKET AND STOCKED UP WI' SUPPLIES.

ARE YE NEEDING A LIFT, HEN? I CAN MOVE ROVER IN BESIDE PORKY AND YE CAN GET A SEAT.

PIGGY JONES, I'VE NO' SEEN YOU FOR AGES. AYE, THAT'D BE THE VERY DAB.

HUP! IN YE COME, ROVER.

MICHTY! ROVER'S THE PIG! GUESS I'M SITTIN' IN THE BACK.

THE MOTOR'S OVERLOADED. WHY DID YE BUY A' THEY TINS O' CURRIED MINCE?

I THOUGHT IT'D GIE MAW A HOLIDAY FRAE COOKING. AND IT WAS BUY TEN TINS, GET TEN FREE. NOW IT SEEMS IT'S THE ENGINE THAT'S COOKING.

THE AIR'S NO' VERY FRESH SITTIN' BACK HERE.

JINGS! HEN'S BEATEN US HERE.

I GOT A PIGGY BACK RIDE.

WELL YOU CAN PIG OOT AGAIN – THERE'S MAIR MINCE HERE THAN IN ONY HOLYROOD REPORT.

HELP MAH BOAB! IT'S HOT CURRY A'RICHT,

NAE WONDER IT WAS CHEAP.

IT'S MELTIN' MY FORK.

IT'S HOTTER THAN GRANPAW'S PEPPERIES.

GOING HAME–

I'M STICKIN' OOT THE SUNROOF WI' MY MOOTH OPEN. IT'S NO' TO GET FRESH AIR – IT'S THE ONLY THING THAT'LL COOL IT DOON.

GO SAFE GLASGOW –
GO SAFE WITH THE BROONS!

THE BROONS HAVE ALWAYS LOOKED AFTER THEIR OWN;
BUT THE NEIGHBOURS THINK GRANPAW'S GOT REASON TO MOAN!

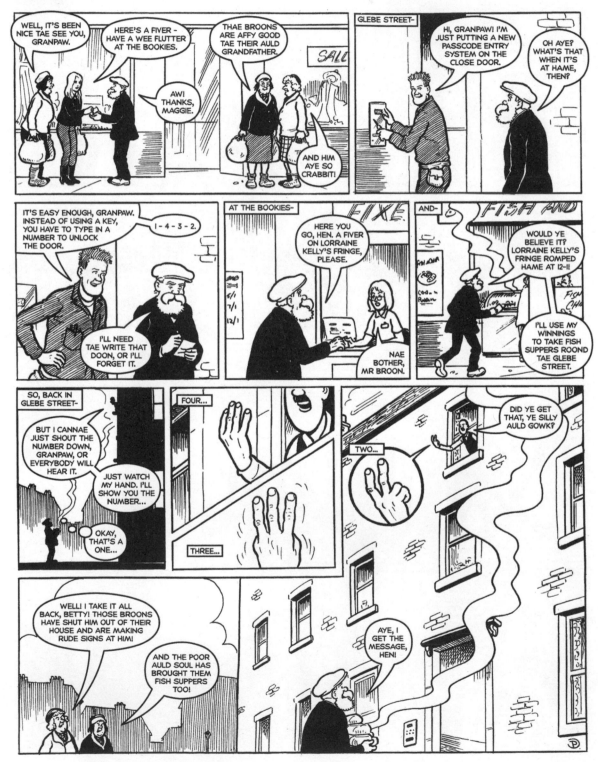

IF YOU NEED REPAIR MEN –
DINNA ASK FOR JOE AND HEN.

DAPHNE'S DANCE CLASS IS IN NEED,
LUCKY HER MAW IS UP TO SPEED.

PAW WANTS HIS WIFE TAE CARE –
IS THE ANSWER BRAND NEW HAIR?

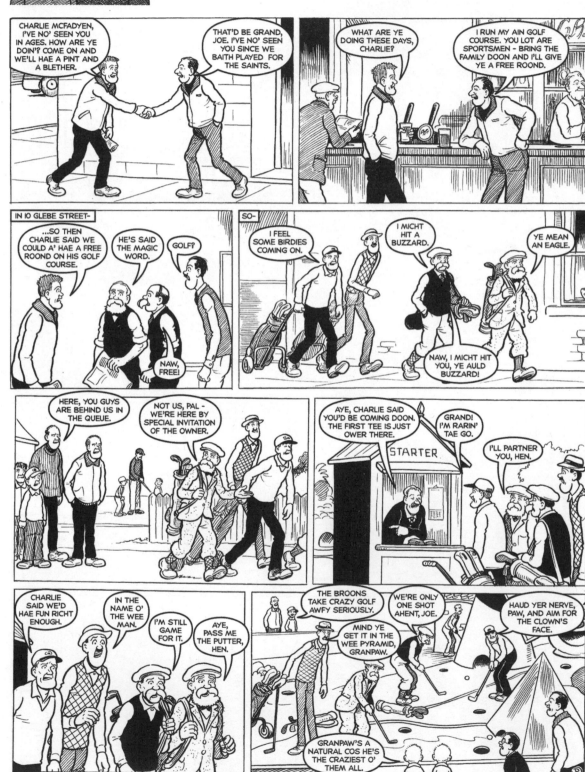

LISTEN NOW AS GRANPAW CROWS
OF A LEGENDARY BROON THAT NOBODY KNOWS.

PAW WORRIES THAT HE'S NO' GOT CASH FOR A BIG BROONS' WEDDING BASH.

STOP FIDGETING AND JUST ENJOY YOUR NIECE'S WEDDING.

I'M GETTING HOT UNDER THE COLLAR THINKING ABOOT WHIT THIS MUST BE COSTING MAH BROTHER.

FIBBER! YOU TIED YOUR BOW TIE OWER TIGHT.

DOESN'T UNCLE TAM LOOK HAPPY WALKING DOON THE AISLE WITH MHAIRI?

BET HE'S HAD A COUPLE O' DRAMS TAE HELP FORGET ABOOT THE BILL.

WHEESHT, YOU!

MHAIRI'S BEAUTIFUL AND THE BRIDESMAIDS ARE SAE BONNIE TAE. SNIFF!

SNIFF! YOU'LL BE A BONNIE BRIDESMAID WHEN I GET MARRIED, DAPHNE.

AYE, I'M SURE WEDDING BELLS WILL COME OOR WAY SOON.

IT'S YOUR TURN TAE WHEESHT, WOMAN. I DINNA LIKE TALK LIKE THAT.

Y'MEAN YER WALLET DISNAE.

WHAT MAKES YOU THINK YOU'LL BE MARRIED BEFORE ME?

BECAUSE I DATE TEN TIMES MAIR BLOKES THAN YOU.

NAEBODY RESPECTS YE IF YE GIE IT AWA TOO EASY.

WHY YOU CHEEKY WITCH...

YOU TWA WHEESHT NOW! THE BRIDE IS LEAVING THE CHURCH.

THE LASS THAT CATCHES THE BRIDE'S BOUQUET WILL BE MARRIED NEXT.

GET YER BIG BAHOOCHIE OUT O' MY WAY THEN.

I HOPE THE NEXT BRIDE WILL BE AS HAPPY AS ME.

OWER HERE, MHAIRI.

OCH! THE SILLY BESOM HAS CHUCKED IT TOO HIGH!

LOOK, I'VE CAUGHT THE NICE FLOOERS.

HA! HA! THAT'LL GIE YE PLENTY TIME TAE SAVE UP FOR A BROONS' FAMILY WEDDING, YE AULD SKINFLINT.

WELL HELD, MAH WEE LAMB.

IF YOUR PAIRTY CLAES ARE A WEE BIT MOTHY - IT DISNAE MATTER AT A MOUNTAIN BOTHY.

GRANPAW'S SANITY IS IN DOUBT.
WHAT'S THE AULD LAD TALKING ABOUT?

DAPHNE LIKES A ROMANTIC NOTE – BUT THIS ONE REALLY GETS HER GOAT!

THE BROON BOYS LOOK LIKE LIARS WHEN THEIR TWIN TRICK BACKFIRES.

GRANPAW BROON IS IN GOOD CHEER,
LOOKING AFTER THE FAMILY BEER.

TO BRING THE CUP BACK TO THE TOON, YE MUST BE SMART LIKE GRANPAW BROON.

IT'S THE AUCHENTOGLE VERSUS AUCHENSHOOGLE CUP FINAL TOMORROW. I'LL BE GLAD WHEN IT'S OVER.

THE LADS ARE AUCHENTOGLE FANS AND MAGGIE IS GOING OOT WI' THE AUCHENSHOOGLE GOALIE.

TRAITOR!

YE'RE A DISGRACE, SISTER!

BAN HER FRAE THE HOOSE.

BOYS! BOYS! HOW DARE YOU INSULT YOUR DEAR SISTER! IT'S ONLY A FITBA GAME.

TAE SAY SORRY I'VE ARRANGED A MEAL FOR YOU AND THE LAD TONIGHT. AND HERE'S MONEY TAE GO CLUBBING LATER.

YOU'RE THE BEST MAN IN THIS HOOSE, GRANPAW.

SO LATER—

THIS IS A BRAW MEAL, MAGGIE. DOUBLE HELPINGS O' EVERYTHING.

AYE, MY GRANPAW KENS THE CHEF.

LATER STILL—

THIS CLUB IS GREAT TAE.

WE CAN STAY TILL IT CLOSES. GRANPAW GAVE ME CASH FOR A LATE TAXI.

NEXT DAY, AT THE CUP FINAL—

GOAL!

THEIR KEEPER NEVER MOVED.

ANOTHER GOAL!

WAKEN UP, TAM!

WE WON THE CUP!

THE AUCHENSHOOGLE KEEPER WAS HALF ASLEEP.

AND HE'S YOUR LAD, MAGGIE?

YAWN! AYE.

YOU'RE A SLY AULD DEEVIL.

I'M SURE I DON'T KNOW WHAT YE MEAN, MRS BROON.

GUESS WHOSE HEADS HANG IN SHAME, AFTER THE LADS' AND LASSIES' FITBA GAME?

IN HIS SEMIT PAW BROON LOOKS PASTY – NAEBODY COULD CALL HIM TASTY.

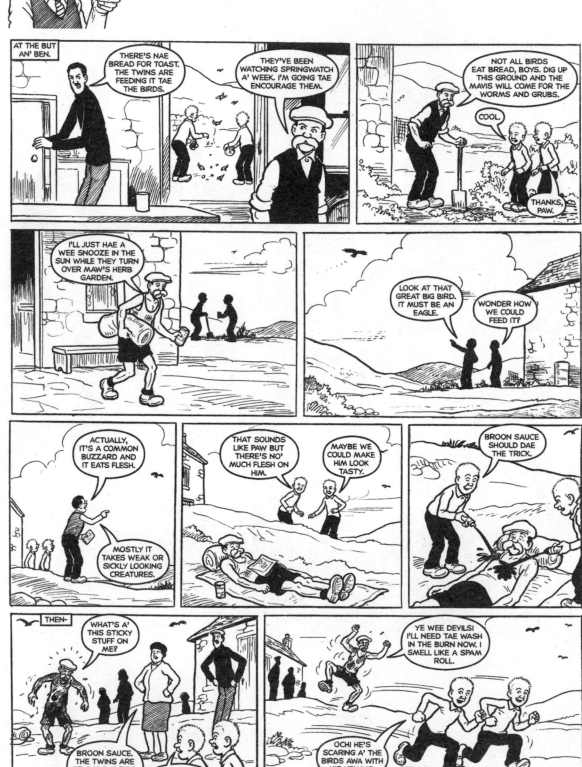

PAW BROON RAVES AND RANTS, OVER A WEE BOX O' PLANTS.

I'M NEEDING WEE MODELS O' FOWK THAT LOOK LIKE ME AND GRANPAW.

WHAT ARE YOU AND GRANPAW UP TAE NOW?

GRANPAW HAS TAE BUILD A NEW GAIRDEN AND IT'S REALLY TINY.

WELL, I KNEW THIS DAY WOULD COME.

THE COONCIL HAVE BEEN WANTING GRANPAW'S ALLOTMENT FOR YEARS TAE BUILD HOOSES ON.

I'M NO' LETTING THEM TAK' HIS ALLOTMENT AND GIE HIM SOME WEE SCRAP O' LAND. I'M GOING TAE FIGHT.

JINGS!

SHORTLY—

WHAT'S THIS I'M HEARING ABOOT YOU BUILDING A NEW GAIRDEN?

I AM THAT AND THESE TWA WEE FIGURES WILL PUT A FINISHING TOUCH TAE IT.

THIS IS OOR PALLET GARDEN WE'VE ENTERED IN GARDENING SCOTLAND AT INGLISTON.

IT'S GRANPAW'S ALLOTMENT BUT TEENY.

OH, DEAR.

AUCHENTOGLE COONCIL OFFICES.

GIVE MY FAITHER HIS GAIRDEN BACK OR I'LL MOLLICATE YE.

WHAT ARE YOU TALKING ABOUT?

CALL THE POLIS. WE'VE A MANIAC HERE.

WE DID REAL WEEL – WE'RE PLACED IN THE PRIZES.

IS PAW COMING TAE SEE WHAT WE'VE DONE?

PAW'S GOT HIMSEL' A WEE ROOM – NO' A WEE GAIRDEN.

INGLE

I DEMAND YE LET ME OOT O' HERE!

YE'LL GET OOT WHEN YOU'VE CALMED DOON, MR BROON.

IN GRANPAW'S EYE THERE'S A STEELY GLINT
- CAN THE AULD LAD REALLY SPRINT?

THE LADIES ARE TOO POSH FOR AUCHENTOGLE TOON – UNTIL THEY MEET UP WI' GRANPAW BROON.

OH, NO! YOUR AUNTS PRIMULA AND PRUDENCE ARE COMING TAE AUCHENTOGLE TODAY.

WHIT? I THOUGHT THEY WERE TOO POSH TAE COME HERE.

I'LL NEED TAE CLEAN AND TIDY THE HOOSE.

GRANPAW SAID HE WAS GOING TAE TAKE CARE OF THEM, MAW.

AS WELL HE MIGHT. THEY ARE HIS SISTERS AFTER ALL.

ARE YOU SURE?

AYE, HE BOUGHT GOODIES IN THE TOON FOR THEM.

WELL, I NEVER. HE DISNAE USUALLY SPEAK TAE THEM.

SHORTLY–

COME AWA IN, LADIES.

STILL LIVING IN THIS CRAMPED HOUSE?

HAVE YOU MADE US TEA WITH YOUR BEST CHINA?

ACTUALLY, YOUR BROTHER IS TAKIN' CARE OF YE TODAY.

OUR BROTHER? WE'VE NOT SEEN HIM SINCE WE WERE CHILDREN.

I RECOGNISE HIM THOUGH – STILL GRUBBY LIKE HE WAS AS A BOY.

THE CHILD IS MISTAKEN – HE'S NOT GOING TO LOOK AFTER US.

TELL THEM, GRANPAW – YOU SAID YOU WERE GOING TAE TREAT THE AUNTS TODAY.

I DID THAT, MY WEE LAMB.

SOMETHING IS RUNNING UP MY LEG!

MY PATHS ARE OVERRUN WI' ANTS. I BOUGHT THIS POWDER TAE TREAT THEM.

AND UNDER MY CORSET!

HA! HA! THAT'S HOW I REMEMBER MY SISTERS – WEE LASSIES RUNNING YELLING DOON THE STREET, BAREFOOT IN THEIR PANTS!

GLEBE STREET, NUMBER TEN – IS NOT FULL OF SCOTS SPORTSMEN.

HERE'S A COMPETITION THAT FITS THE BILL,
AND TESTS OOT HEN'S UNUSUAL SKILL.

YOU SHOULD BE TRAINING WI' ME, HEN. WE'RE IN THE TUG O' WAR TEAM FOR THE TURRIFF SHOW LATER.

I CANNA, I'VE TAE FETCH BACK MY CAR – IT BROKE DOON AGAIN.

WHAUR'S HEN NOW? WE'RE SUPPOSED TAE BE GOING FOR A TRAINING RUN.

HE'S HAVING TAE PUSH HIS CAR HAME.

THAT'S EVERY NIGHT THIS WEEK THAT CAR HAS MADE YOU MISS TRAININ'. YOU'RE DRAPPED FRAE THE TEAM.

PECH!

YOU AND ME WILL ENTER AN EVENT AT THE TURRIFF SHOW, BROTHER.

WE'RE NO' EXACTLY ATHLETES, HORACE.

LATER, IN 'TURRA'.

I'LL GO AND GET US ENTERED.

TURRIFF SHOW

I THOUGHT YOU'D BE GOOD AT THE BIG BALE PUSH, HEN.

YOU'RE A CLEVER ANE, HORACE. I'VE SPENT WEEKS PUSHIN' MY CAR A' OWER THE PLACE.

START

MICHTY! HEN AND HORACE ARE FAIR FLEEIN' ALONG.

HA! HA! THIS IS A DODDLE TAE PUSH AFTER THAT AULD MOTOR OF MINE.

FIN

TURRIFF SHOW BIG BALE PUSH CHAMPIONS ARE TEAM BROON!

JINGS! WE'RE SPORTSMEN, HORACE.

BIG BALE CHAMPS

LAST PLACE IN THE TUG O' WAR ARE THE AUCHENTOGLE TUGGERS.

GASP!

BAD LUCK, JOE. MAYBE I SHOULD LEND YOU MY CAR.

CAN THE POWER OF HORACE'S PEN IMPRESS HIS BROTHERS, JOE AND HEN?

BRODIES' TEA SEEMS A TASTY TREAT –
SO WHY'S GRANPAW DECIDED TAE VOTE WAE HIS FEET?

GRUMPY PAW SAYS ENOUGH'S ENOUGH –
BUT HE STILL CANNAE SWITCH THE TELLY AFF!

TIME FLIES FAST INDEED,
WHEN YOU'RE ENJOYING A GOOD READ.

THE TROUBLE WI' A CLASSIC CAR
IS THAT YE MICHT NO' GET VERY FAR.

I'VE BOUCHT MYSEL' A CLASSIC SPORTS CAR. IT'LL GO UP IN VALUE INSTEAD OF DOON.

I HAD ANE LIKE THAT BACK IN 1952.

DID YE LIKE IT?

I SWORE BY IT, HEN.

I'VE STILL GOT THE GLOVES THAT CAME WITH IT.

WOW! THE GENUINE ARTICLE. THAT'S COOL.

THEY'RE NO' DRIVING GLOVES – I CANNA FEEL THE STEERING WHEEL WHEN I'M WEARING THEM.

I DIDNAE SAY THEY WERE.

HELLO, LADIES! FANCY A SPIN IN MY CLASSIC CAR?

SORRY, HEN, I'M WASHING MY HAIR.

AND THAT'S A CLASSIC PUT DOON. HA! HA!

EEEEK!

BANG!

HELP MAH BOAB!

MY CAR'S CONKED OOT! I THOUGHT YOU SAID YOU SWORE BY THIS TYPE O' CAR, GRANPAW?

AYE, I SWORE BY IT, BELOW IT, ABOVE IT BUT MOSTLY AT IT!

THAT'S WHY I GAVE YE THE GLOVES, LADDIE.

THEY KEPT MY HANDS WARM WHILE I PUSHED THE CAR HAME.

MUTTER! YOU JUST STEER IT.

PECH!

HAS DAPHNE GONE COMPLETELY MAD – OR WILL HER FOOTPRINTS LAND A LAD?

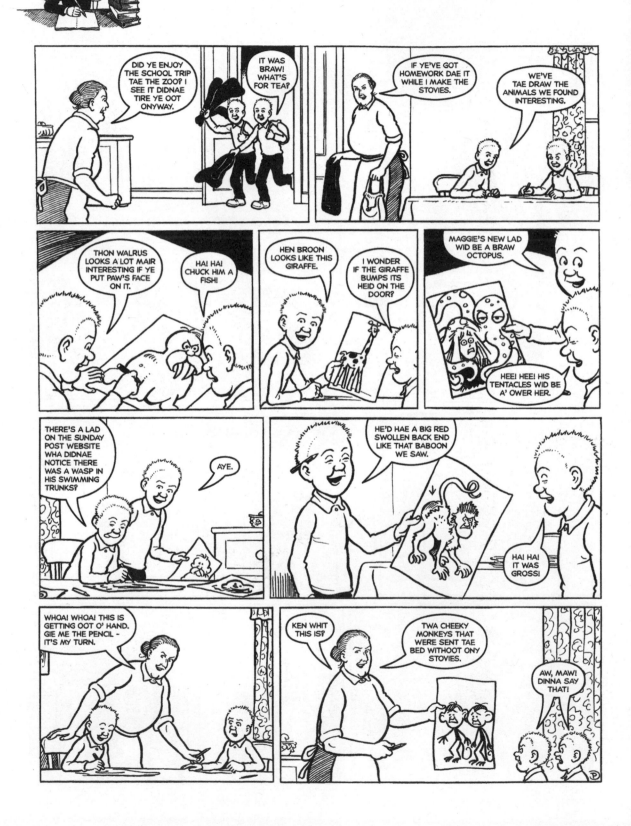

WILL MAW SHED THE TEARS
WHEN HER FAVOURITE PAINTING DISAPPEARS?

LISTEN TAE THE SHRIEKS,
PAW BROON'S WITHOOT BREEKS.

DAPHNE'S NEW POSH LAD
HAS NEVER HEARD LANGUAGE THAT BAD.

GRANPAW'S FEELING AWFY SMUG, AFTER BETTING TIPS FROM A DUG!

THE MEENISTER HAS IT PLANNED,
THAT THE GOSSIPS WILL BE BANNED.

IT'S ENOUGH TAE MAKE YE SCREAM – A NICHT WITHOOT A TV SCREEN.

THE LADS ARE REALLY GETTING THE HANG,
OF A CHRISTMAS THAT GOES WITH A BANG.

PAW LANDS THE HOOSE IN A PLIGHT, CHRISTMAS TIME AND THERE'S NAE LIGHT.

YOU MUST OBEY CERTAIN LAWS –
WHEN SENDING A LETTER TAE SANTA CLAUS.

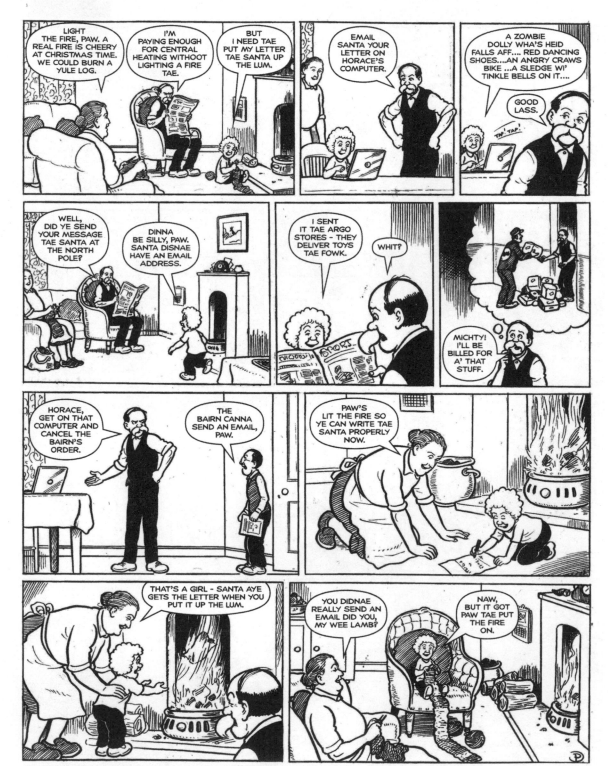

THIS CHRISTMAS TREE IS HARD TAE BEAT -
IT COMES WI' A FINE FREE HEAT.

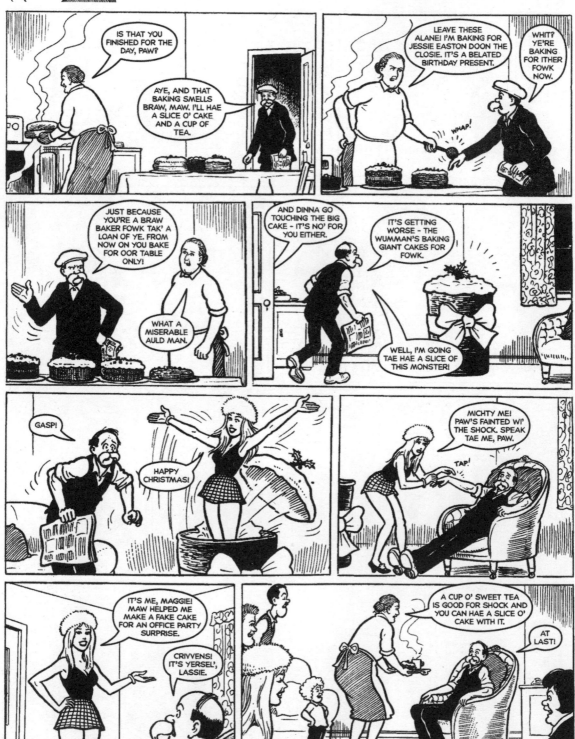

AFTER CHRISTMAS MONEY'S TIGHT,
THE BILLS ARE MAKING A DREADFUL SIGHT.

PLEASE ENJOY THIS CLASSIC TALE,
FOR HAPPY TIMES, THE BROONS DON'T FAIL.

MAW'S GIFT SETS HER BIG HEART SINKING,
UNTIL HER MAN DOES SOME FAST THINKING.

EVERY FAMILY HAS ITS UPS AND DOONS - ESPECIALLY THE FAMOUS HAPPY BROONS.

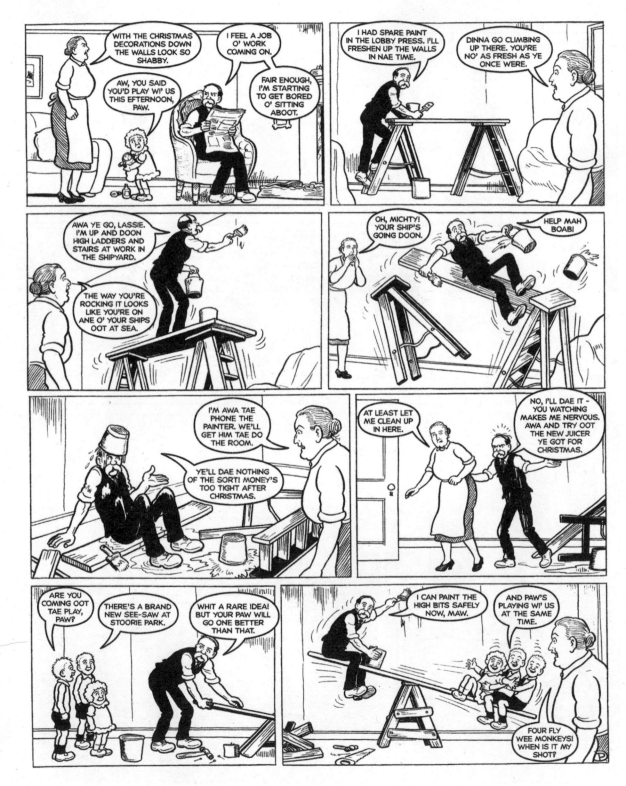